Bookworm
Contents

Information Skills

Language, Mechanics, and Usage Lessons

BOOK 1

Learning About Words and Pictures

(At this level, some children may need help reading and following directions. Provide support as necessary.)

Read the story below. Then answer the questions on the next page. Talk about the story with a friend and tell how you knew the answers.

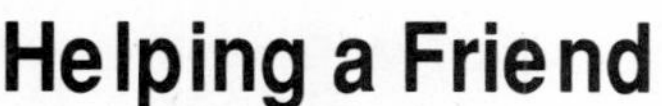

Helping a Friend

"Come down, Jim," called Teddy. "I need you to help me find my glasses."

"What are glasses?" asked Jim.

"You know," said Teddy. "Glasses are the things that I use to see better."

"I don't need to come down, Teddy," said Jim.

"Why not?" asked Teddy.

Jim said, "I can help you from here. Just reach up and touch the top of your head!"

"Oh," said Teddy in a little voice. "Thanks."

(Sample answers)

1. Who are Teddy and Jim?

Teddy is a bear.

Jim is an owl.

2. What did Teddy want Jim to do?

He wanted Jim to help him find his glasses.

3. Why didn't Jim need to come down?

He could see Teddy's glasses from his tree.

4. Where were Teddy's glasses?

They were on his head!

5. How do you think Teddy was feeling when he touched his glasses?

He felt a little bit silly.

Learning About Vowel Pairs

Read the story, using what you know about vowel sounds to help you figure out the underlined words. Then answer the questions.

At the Train Stop

"Let's wait here," said Gail. "Soon we'll see the train coming."

"I know all about trains," said Jack. "A train runs on rails. Trains can carry mail and other things. People ride on trains, but they have to pay."

"I see the train coming now," said Gail. "Let's stand back, out of the way."

(Sample answers)

1. What are Gail and Jack waiting for?

They are waiting for a train.

2. What is one thing Jack knows about trains?

Answers will vary.

3. Why does Gail want them to stand back?

She wants them to be out of the way of the train.

The Surprise

Decide which word completes each sentence. Circle it, then print it in the lines.

already   send   idea

1. Paul had an idea.

present   town   still

2. He wanted to send his sister a present.

sure   box   town

3. Paul went to a store in town.

already   nothing   spent

4. The store had nothing but baskets!

plain   present   burned

5. The baskets looked too plain.

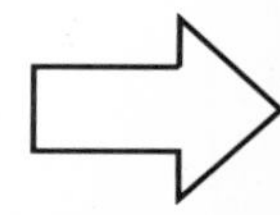

town spent (box)

6. Paul found a special box in another store.

seemed (opened) burned

7. When it was opened, the box played a song.

(sure) already still

8. Paul was sure his sister would like the box.

burn open (send)

9. Now all he had to do was send it to her.

Learning About Vowel Pairs

Read the story. If the letters *ea* in an underlined word stand for the short *e* sound, write the word under **Short *e***. If the letters *ea* stand for the long *e* sound, write the word under **Long *e*.**

> The weather this winter is so cold. Even with two sweaters I'm cold. But that bird's happy. His feathers keep out the cold. Last summer we picked peaches to eat from that tree. What a nice summer treat that would be right now!

Short *e*	**Long *e***
weather	peaches
sweaters	eat
feathers	treat

My Five Senses

Decide which word completes each sentence. Circle it, then print it in the lines. When you are finished, you will have a poem!

taste important (game)

1. It's great to play in a game at night.

(stars) each only

2. The stars in the sky are a beautiful sight.

eyes (moon) water

3. Under the moon I feel just right.

ears (ball) taste

4. Now my arms are tired from catching the

ball.

(fingers) stars less

5. My fingers are as cold as wind in the fall.

many game (minute)

6. But in less than a minute, I know Mom will call.

Time to come in for the night, one and all!

Learning About Word Endings

Read each sentence. Each underlined word is a base word with an ending. Circle the ending and write the base word in the lines next to the sentence.

(You may want to remind children that some base words are changed before endings are added.)

1. An elephant is a wonderful helper for people. — help

2. An elephant is one of the strongest animals. — strong

3. It is bigger than a horse. — big

4. Lifting trees is not a problem for elephants. — lift

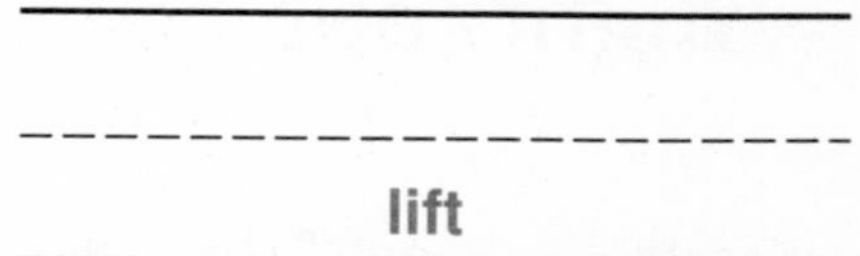

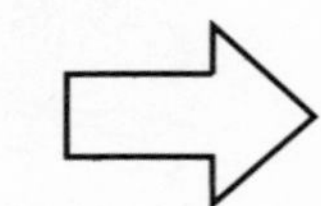

5. An owner of an elephant takes care of it.

own

6. An elephant needs water and food.

need

7. It eats lots of hay and other plants.

eat

8. Giving food to an elephant can be fun!

give

9. Don't you wish you owned an elephant?

own

Learning About Vowel Pairs

Decide which word completes each sentence. Circle it, then print it in the lines.

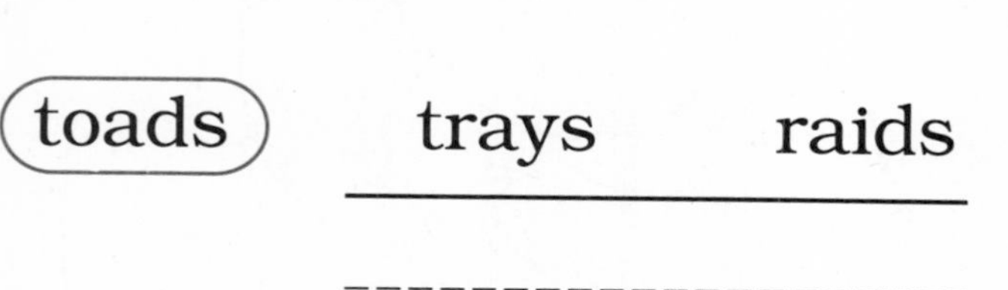

(toads) trays raids

1. Some tiny toads went walking.

ray (road) load

2. They hurried down the road.

soap seat (soak)

3. The toads wanted to soak in some cold water.

(float) moan fail

4. Some toads liked to just float.

coat (croak) treat

5. The toads were so happy they started to croak.

Geraldine's Big Snow

Decide which word completes each sentence. Circle it, then print it in the lines.

heard (hard) start

1. It's hard for birds to find food in winter.

stop park (shop)

2. Don bought bird food at the pet shop.

(park) cloud start

3. He went to the park and waited quietly.

high park (clouds)

4. Suddenly, he looked up at the clouds.

count (sky) soft

5. He saw many birds in the sky.

hand soft front

6. The birds came down and stopped in

front of Don.

cloud counted bought

7. He counted seven birds.

shopping hungry hand

8. Don thought the birds might be hungry.

brought stopped wait

9. He brought out the bird food.

quietly heard started

10. When the birds saw the food, they

started to eat.

Reading New Words

Read the sentences. Then look at the pictures next to each sentence. Circle the picture that tells about the sentence.

1. That's a great noisemaker!
2. You shouldn't sit there!
3. Bill plays with his new trains.
4. Abby has a heavy sweater.
5. Now everyone will have ice cream.

Now write a sentence of your own to answer this question.

What would you like to eat for a special treat?

Answers will vary.

BOOK 2

This Old Man

These sentences tell a story about a funny race. Decide which word completes each sentence. Print it in the lines.

eight	ten	stick	roll	line

1. Put your running shoes on this line.

2. Listen as I count to ten. Then run!

3. You must jump over eight boxes.

4. Then you must roll down the hill.

5. Finally, you must jump over this stick.

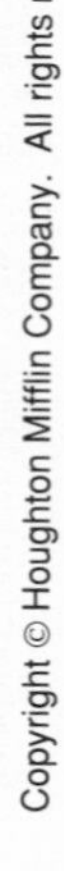

Some of the words you are learning have more than one meaning. Read the sentences below. Print each sentence next to the picture it tells about.

Pat eats a **roll** that he baked.
Pat will **roll** down the hill.

Pat will roll down the hill.

Pat eats a roll that he baked.

Pat's rolls **stick** to the pan.
Pat's dog gets the **stick**.

Pat's rolls stick to the pan.

Pat's dog gets the stick.

What Happens First, Next, and Last

Read this story.

Once there were three Billy Goats named Gruff. They all wanted to eat the grass that grew on the other side of the river. To get there, they had to cross a bridge. But a mean troll lived under it.

First, Little Billy Goat Gruff tried to cross the bridge. He saw Troll waiting to eat him and said, "My brother will make a much bigger dinner for you!" So Troll let him cross.

Next, Big Billy Goat Gruff began to cross the bridge. When he saw Troll, he said, "My brother will make an even bigger dinner for you." So Troll let him cross.

At last, Biggest Billy Goat Gruff began to cross the bridge. When he saw Troll, he put down his head and pushed Troll into the river. And that mean troll never stopped the goats again.

These sentences about the story are in the wrong order. Write the number 1, 2, or 3 beside each sentence to show what happened first, next, and last.

__2__ The troll let Big Billy Goat Gruff cross the bridge.

__3__ Biggest Billy Goat Gruff pushed Troll into the river.

__1__ The troll let Little Billy Goat Gruff cross the bridge.

Learning About Vowel Pairs

Decide which word completes each sentence. Circle it, then print it in the lines. Read the whole story to a friend.

news boots brooms

1. I put on my ___boots___ and walked down to the pond.

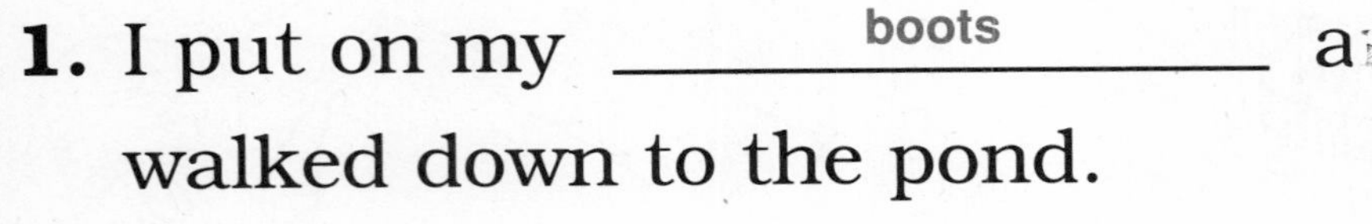

grew droop goose

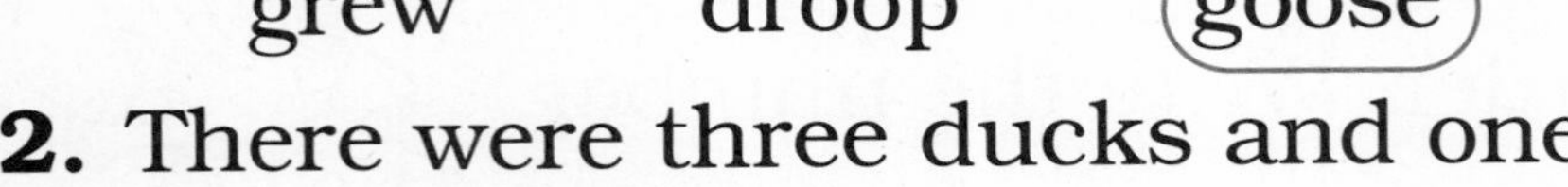

2. There were three ducks and one ___goose___ at the pond.

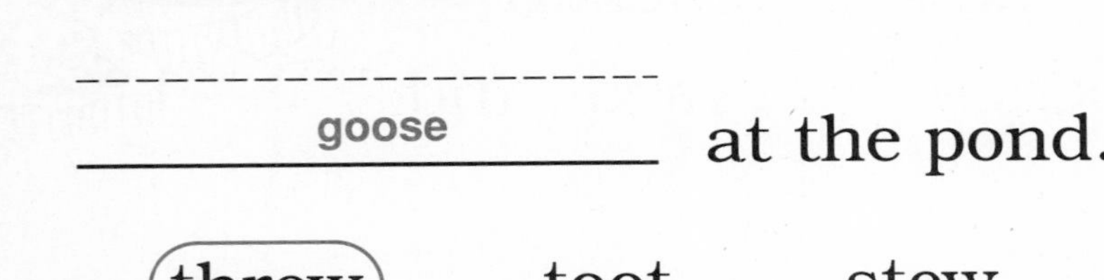

threw toot stew

3. I ___threw___ out a few pieces of bread for them to eat.

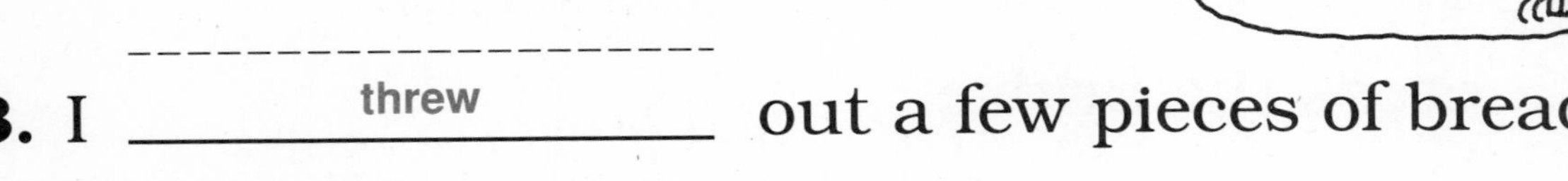

crew chew blew

4. The ducks ate so fast because they don't have to ___chew___.

Stone Soup

Decide which word completes each sentence. Circle it, then print it in the lines.

young enough began

1. Once upon a time there was

a young king.

set stone thin

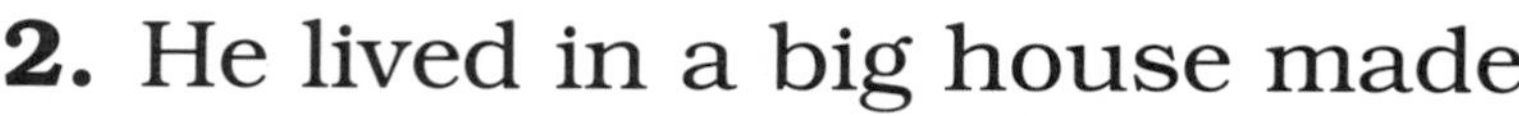

2. He lived in a big house made

of stone.

thick road think

3. One day the king's cook baked some

nice, thick bread for the king.

butter better because

4. "How can I eat this bread without

butter?" asked the king.

stone (set) fit

5. The king's cook ___set___ out to find some butter.

(lady) later nice

6. He soon saw a young ___lady___ coming down the road.

began enough (filled)

7. She was carrying a basket ___filled___ with things to eat.

young gray (yellow)

8. "My lady, have you any good ___yellow___ butter?" asked the cook.

finger (fit) fill

9. "I have," said the lady, "and it's ___fit___ for a king!"

Learning About Vowel Pairs

First, read the story below.

When the snow is gone, we will plant flowers. First, Dad will plow deep down into the ground. Then we will plant the seeds in rows. They will be all around the house. When the flowers grow, they will be beautiful! We will have the best garden in town.

Next, print the underlined words that have the vowel sound you hear in brown and cloud.

plow	down	ground
around	house	town

Now print the underlined words that have the vowel sound you hear in the word know.

snow	rows	grow

Words That Stand for Other Words

Read each pair of sentences. In the lines below the sentences, write who or what the underlined words stand for.

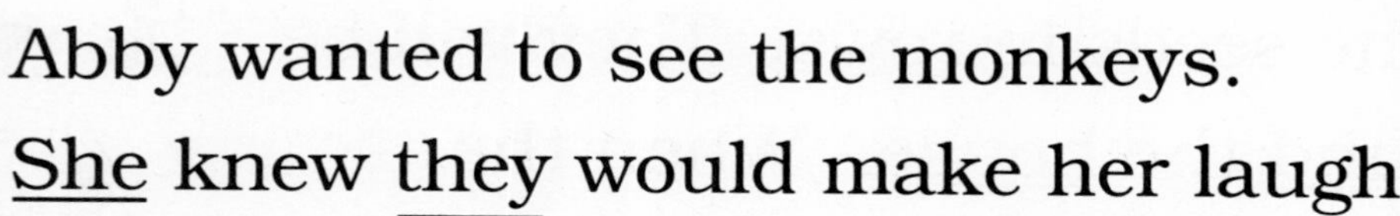

Abby wanted to see the monkeys.
She knew they would make her laugh.

1. She stands for Abby.

2. The word they stands for the monkeys.

Max couldn't wait to see the elephants.
He had bought some food for them.

3. He stands for Max.

4. The word them stands for the elephants.

Learning About Vowel Pairs

What Do You Think?

First, read each unfinished question. Then write the word from the box that best finishes it.

blow	books	mouse	pool	down

1. Is a cat afraid of a mouse ?

2. Do you like to read books ?

3. Did the wind blow that tree down ?

4. Do you like to swim in a pool ?

Now write a question of your own. Use one of the words in the box.

food	threw	clown	pound

Answers will vary.

The Three Little Pigs

Read the story below.

Abby and Ted live on a farm. Last summer their mom and dad sent them to the fair.

So many good things happened at the fair! Ted had fun playing games. He tried to throw a ball into a well full of water, and he did it on the third try!

Abby ran in a race. She ran so quickly that she won second prize. The prize was a puppy with red hair. "We can build a house for him," said Ted.

Abby had money with her. She and Ted bought their mom and dad a present. Then they went home for dinner.

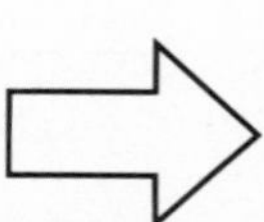

Answer these questions about the story. Print the answers in the lines. Then talk about your answers with a friend. (Sample answers)

1. Where did Abby and Ted go last summer?

They went to the fair.

2. What happened when Ted played a game?

He won on the third try.

3. How did Abby win second prize?

She ran quickly in a race.

4. What did Ted want to build?

a house for Abby's puppy

5. What did Abby do with her money?

She bought a present.

Reading New Words

In the box are some lines from other old favorites. Read each line, then print it next to the picture it tells about. Read the page to a friend. Tell how you figured out the underlined words.

Mother Goose
The Biggest Billy Goat Gruff
The cow jumped over the moon
The sheep's in the meadow
The king was in the countinghouse

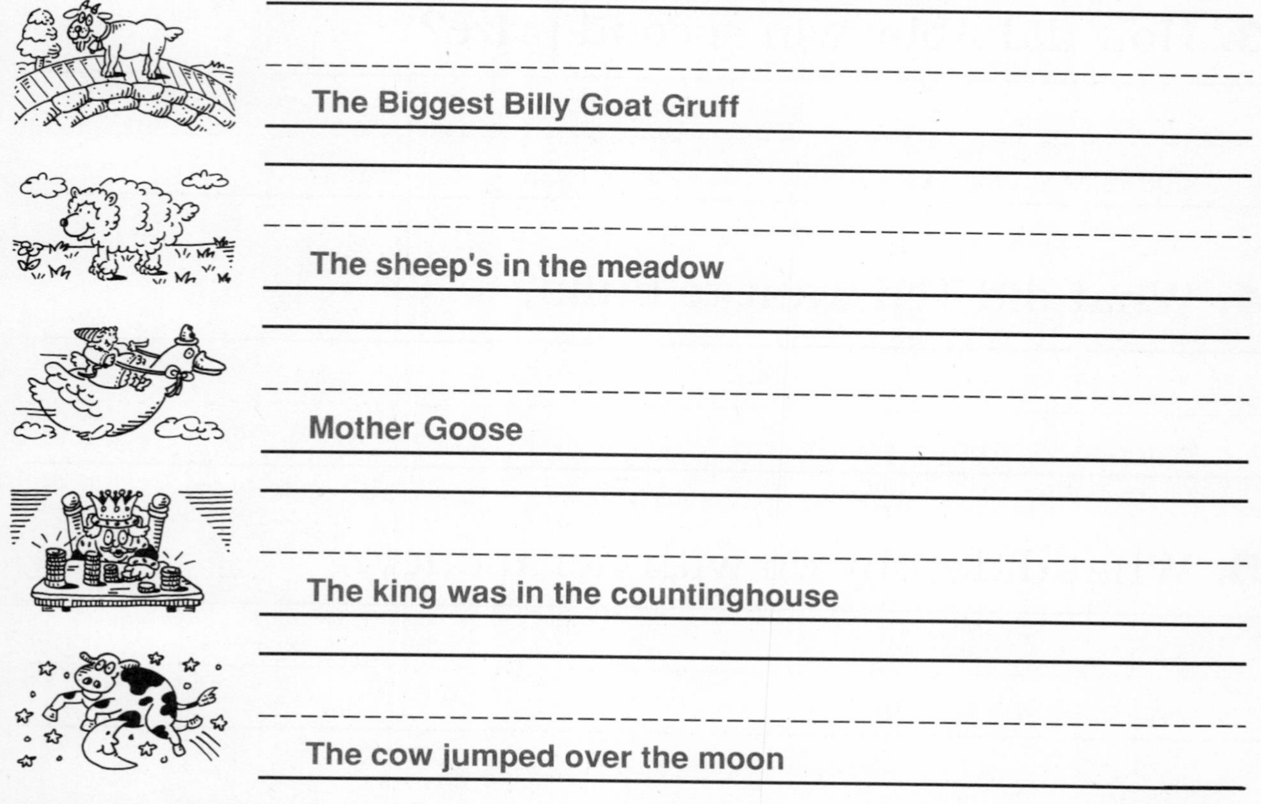

The Biggest Billy Goat Gruff

The sheep's in the meadow

Mother Goose

The king was in the countinghouse

The cow jumped over the moon

BOOK 3

Learning About Vowels

Circle the word that completes each sentence. Then print it in the lines.

cubs cubes

1. Fred and Buddy are bear cubs.

pin pine

2. They built a house in a pine tree.

beet bet

3. "I'll bet this old box will make a great chair," said Fred.

mop mope

4. "I'll use this mop to clean up," said Buddy.

tap tape

5. "Now I'll tape this picture up, and we'll have a nice clubhouse!" said Fred.

Learning About Story Problems

Read the story. Then answer the questions about it on the next page.

The Farmer and His Three Boys

There once were three boys who lived on their father's farm. The boys didn't work together very well. Each one said he didn't need any help from the others.

The father thought and thought about what to do. One day, he asked each boy to find a thick stick. The boys brought the sticks to their father.

"Which one of you is strong enough to break all three sticks at once?" he asked. Not one of the boys could break all three.

Then the father gave one stick to each boy. "Now try again," he said. And each boy found that he could break one stick. Together they broke all three.

"When the three of you work together," the father said, "you can do something that you couldn't do all alone."

(Sample answers)

1. What problem does the farmer have?

His boys don't work well together.

2. What does the father use to solve the problem?

The father uses three sticks.

3. What does he ask the boys to do?

He asks them to break all three sticks at once.

4. What did the boys find out about working together?

They could do something together that each one couldn't do all alone.

Learning About Contractions

Read each sentence. The two underlined words can be changed to a contraction. Find the correct contraction in the box. Then print it in the lines next to the sentence.

What's	you'd	
I'd	She'll	isn't

1. Mom is not here now. isn't

2. She will be home soon. She'll

3. If you would like, I'll tell her you called. you'd

4. What is your name, please? What's

5. I had better write it down. I'd

Bailey Goes Camping

Use this page to tell about yourself. Write an ending for each sentence. Share your page with a friend when you are finished.

1. The time of year I like best is Answers will vary.

2. On hot days, I like to Answers will vary.

3. The names of a few of my friends are Answers will vary.

4. The foods I like best are Answers will vary.

5. I smile when Answers will vary.

Learning About Word Endings

Read each sentence. Each underlined word is a base word with an ending. Circle the ending and write the base word in the lines next to the sentence.

1. Turtle and Rabbit were running in a race. run

2. Turtle was moving as fast as he could. move

3. But that wasn't very fast, because he carried his house on his back! carry

4. After a while he stopped and looked for Rabbit. stop

(You may want to remind children that some base words are changed before endings are added.)

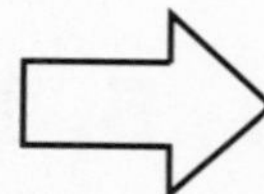

5. Rabbit had stopped, too. He was looking sadder than he ever had.

sad

6. "I'm getting too tired to run," said Rabbit sadly. "I want to go home."

get

7. Suddenly Turtle was happy that he was carrying his house.

Sudden

8. "I *am* home!" Turtle said. He smiled and smiled.

smile

Jimmy Lee Did It

Decide which word completes each sentence. Circle it, then print it in the lines.

trouble (trip) wall

1. Mom was going away on a trip.

(leave) break trip

2. My little brother didn't want Mom to leave.

won't (since) caused

3. She hadn't been away overnight since he was a baby.

leave (apart) painted

4. He didn't like to be apart from Mom.

(trouble) trip breaking

5. I was sure my brother was going to make trouble!

floor leave (cause)

6. "He won't cause problems if you play with him," Mom said.

(won't) wall since

7. "I guess that won't be hard to do," I said.

paints (breaks) leaves

8. "Just make sure that nothing breaks!" Mom said.

breaking caused (painting)

9. "We'll do a lot of painting," I said.

trip (walls) leaves

10. "OK. Just make sure that he doesn't paint the walls!" said Mom.

Anna's Secret Friend

First, read this story. Then print in the lines the word that completes each sentence.

Emma and Jimmy have made their own writing paper. Both children are pleased with their work. Emma has written her name in bright red letters. Jimmy's writing paper has small stars on it.

The children like to write letters. Emma is going to write a short letter to her friend Kim. She hopes Kim will come to stay overnight. Jimmy will write to his friend Mark, who is away. He wants Mark to know that he misses him.

Kim and Mark will be very happy to get those letters from Emma and Jimmy! Perhaps Kim and Mark will write back.

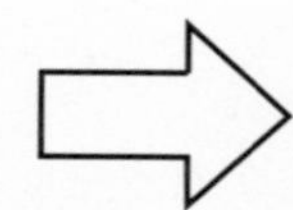

perhaps paper both

1. Emma and Jimmy made some writing paper.

slowly short yet

2. Emma will write a short letter to Kim, asking her to stay overnight.

missing money loud

3. Jimmy will write to say he's missing his friend Mark.

Showed Paper Perhaps

4. Perhaps Kim and Mark will write back soon.

Reading New Words

Read each sentence. Circle the picture that shows what the sentence is about. Read the page to a friend and tell how you figured out the underlined words.

1. Ted had made a lunchtime surprise for his mom.

2. He'd cooked some eggs.

3. He'd put some buttered toast on the plate.

4. He'd put some flowers in a vase.

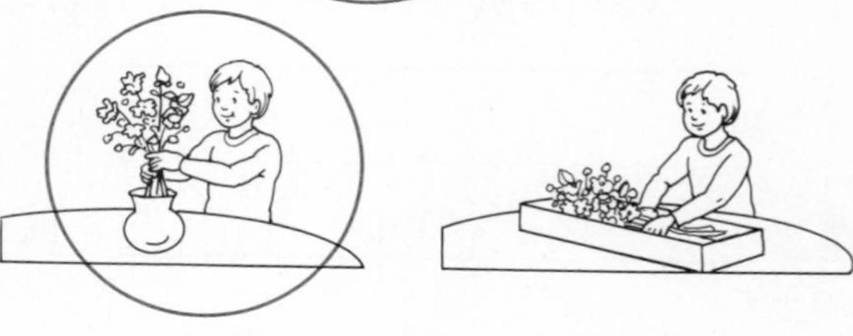

5. Then Ted made up a funny song to call his mom into the kitchen.

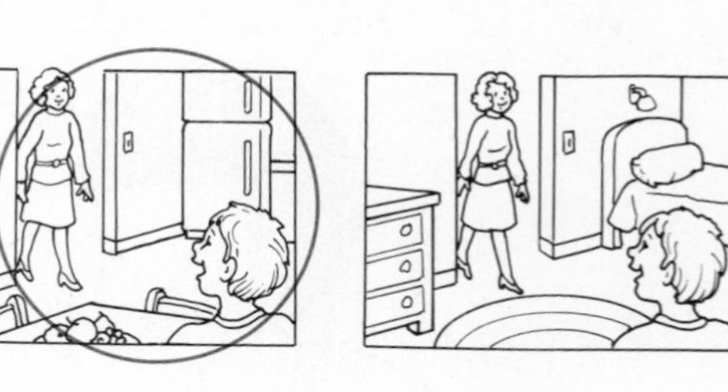

What do you like to eat for lunch?

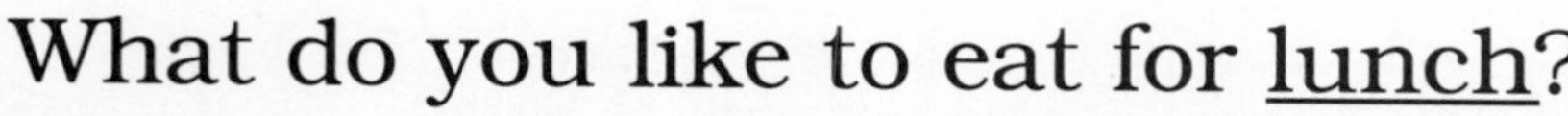

Answers will vary.

ABC Order

Underline the first letter in each word. In each box, number the words **1, 2, 3,** or **4** to show ABC order.

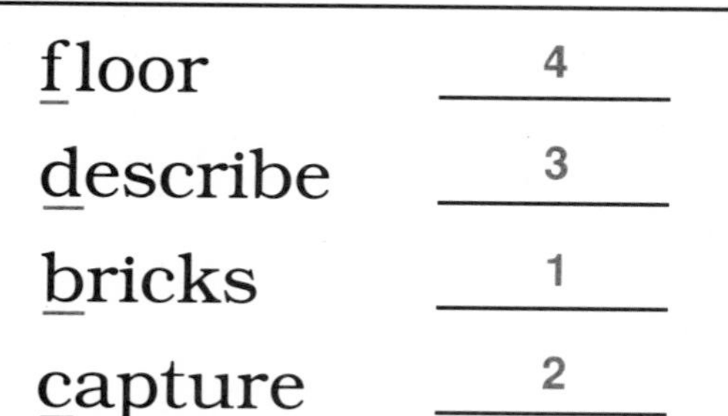

floor	4
describe	3
bricks	1
capture	2

shoe	2
trouble	3
radio	1
unfamiliar	4

nothing	3
mystery	2
open	4
library	1

Now look up the words from the boxes in the glossary at the back of your reader. See if you put them in the right order. Before you look up each word, think about where in the glossary you would find it—the beginning, middle, or end.

Learning About Picture Maps

Follow the directions below. Find out where you will end up. Draw the route you would follow on the map.

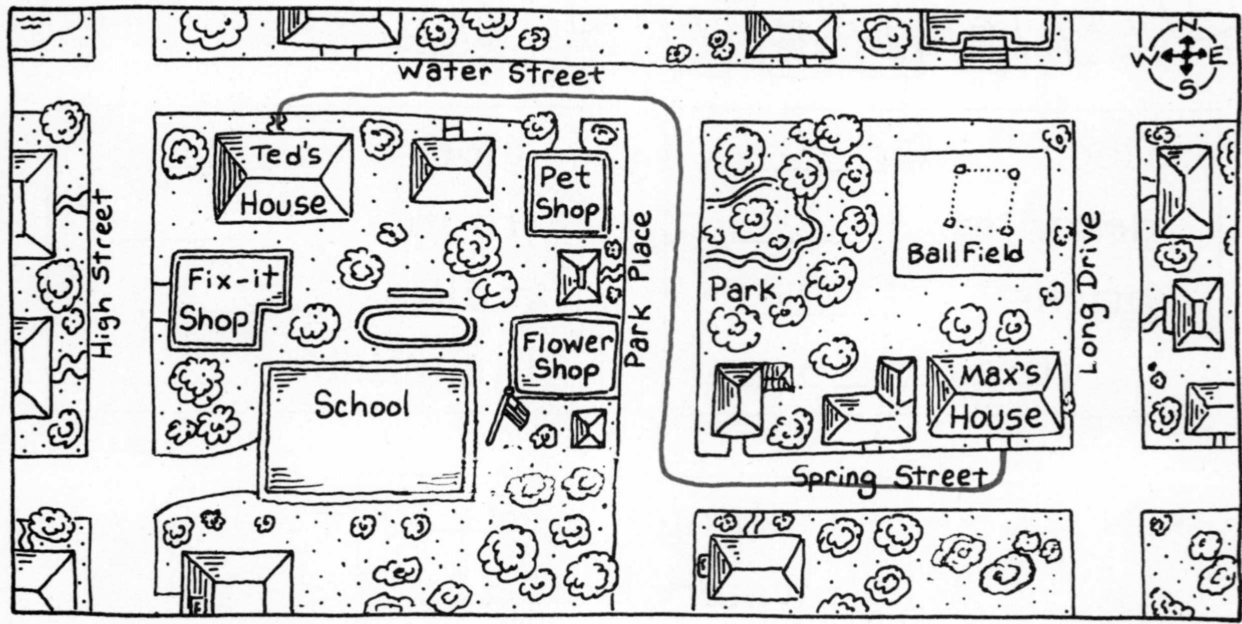

1. Start at Ted's house. From there, go to the pet shop on Water Street.
2. After the pet shop, turn onto Park Place.
3. Go past the flower shop. Then turn onto Spring Street.
4. Go to the third house on Spring Street. Where did you end up?

Max's house

Naming Words

Some words are **naming words.** (Use the suggestions on page 68 to model the lesson and guide children through the pages.)

boy	hat	park
dog	frog	book

 Write the naming words for these pictures.

1. dog

4. hat

2. book

5. park

3. boy

6. frog

Trace the naming words for the pictures.

(Read the directions with children and encourage them to complete this page independently.)

1.

hat

2.

pig

3.

man

4.

fox

5.

bed

6.

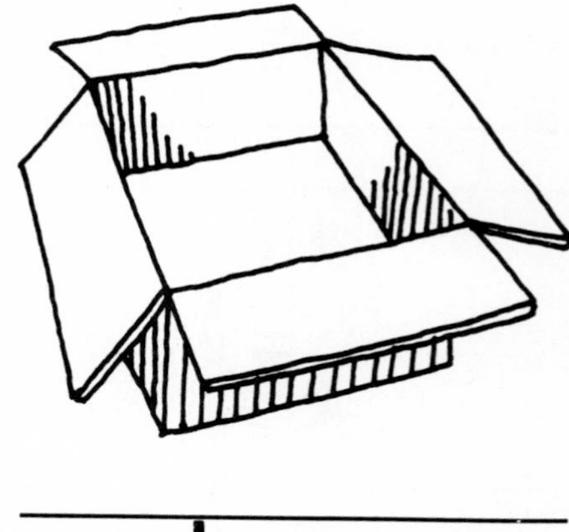

box

Naming Words in Sentences

Naming words name **people, animals, things,** and **places.**

Finish the sentences. Use naming words from the word box.

children	street	cat

1. My pet cat is black.
2. The children like school.
3. I like the houses on my street.

Write a naming word for each sentence.

1. The fox is quiet.
2. SCHOOL BUS I saw the school bus.

 Finish the sentences. Trace the naming words.

bear

1. The bear is big.

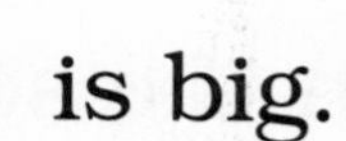

cap

2. My cap is on the table.

plant

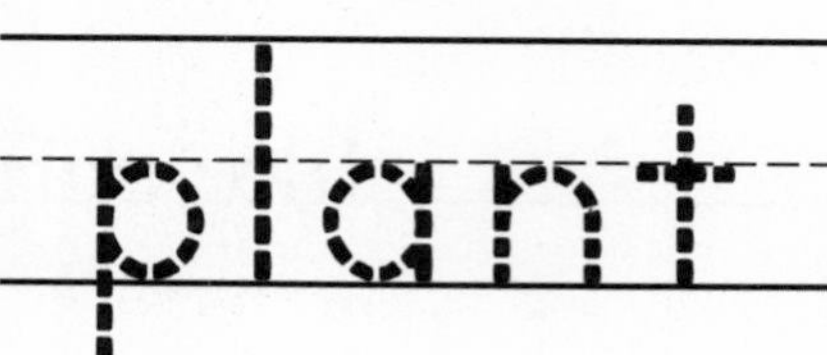

3. This plant needs sun.

man

4. The man waits for a bus.

park

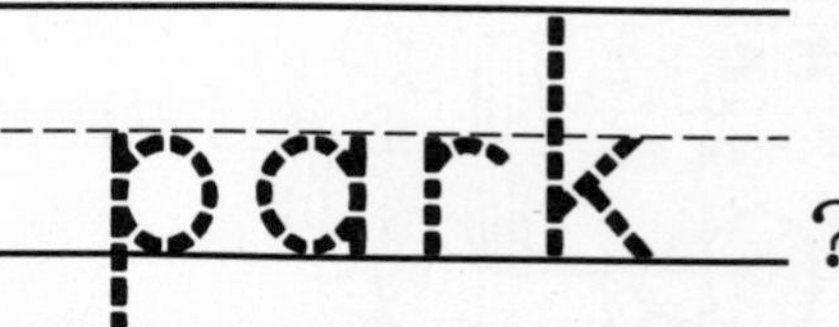

5. May we go to the park?

One and More Than One

Some naming words mean one.

boat	

Some naming words mean more than one.

boat**s**	

An **s** means more than one.

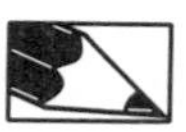 Draw a picture for each word below.

book**s**	tree**s**	flower**s**
1.	**3.**	**5.**
ball	key**s**	pen
2.	**4.**	**6.**

Match the words with the pictures.

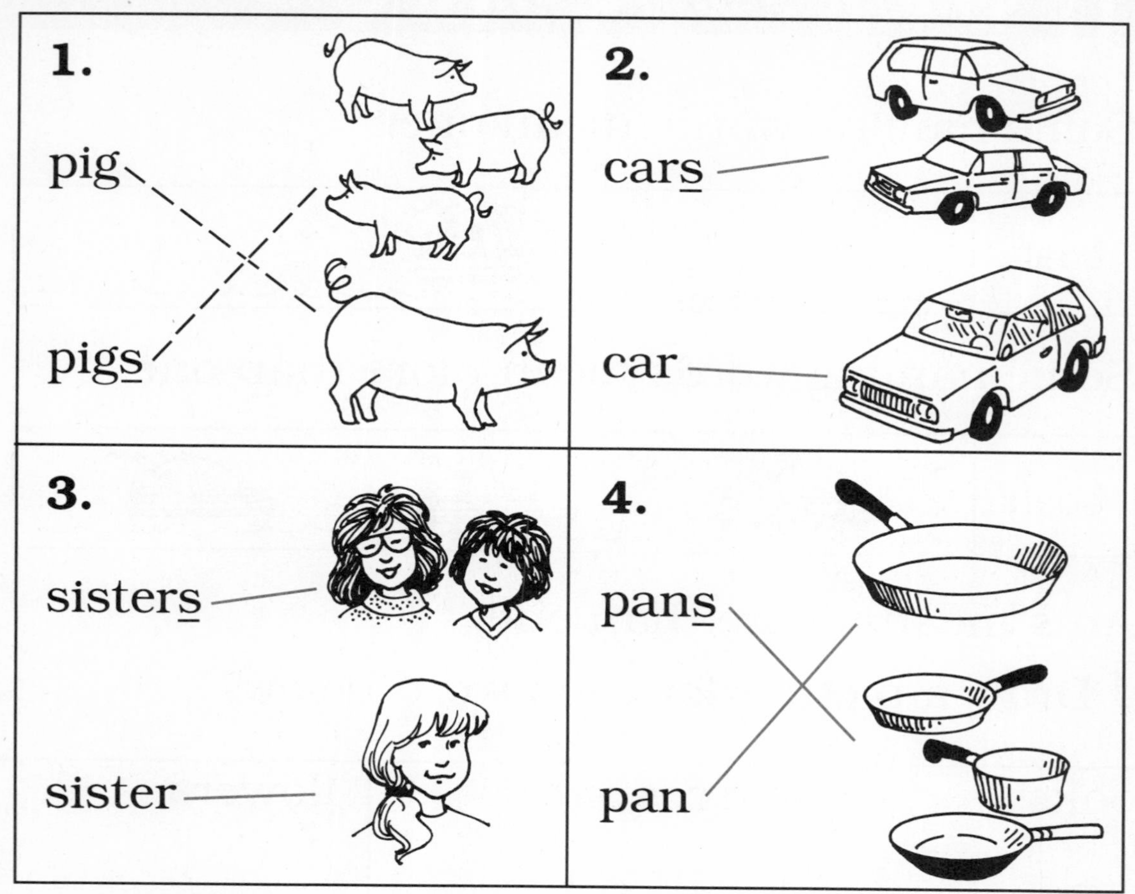

Circle the words that mean more than one.
Trace the words.

Special Names

People have **special names.**

Places have **special names.**

Some **animals** have **special names.**

Carol
Ben
Freed **P**ark
Ruff

A **special name** begins with a **capital letter.**
Write the special name the right way.

1. ron Ron

Ron

2. fluffy Fluffy

Fluffy

3. Ann ann

Ann

4. denver Denver

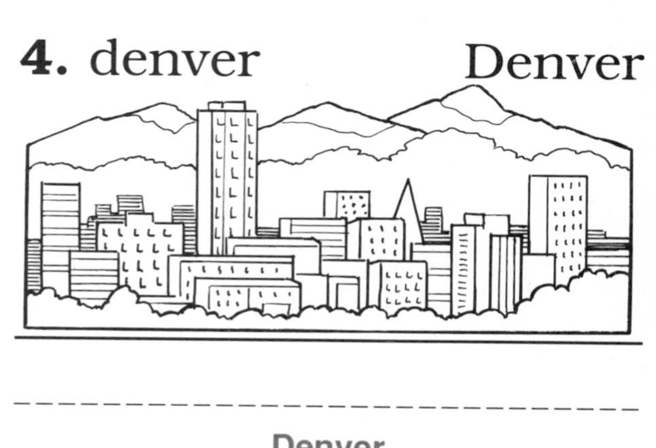

Denver

 Trace the special names.

1. 

Jean

Jean

2. 

Ruff

Ruff

3. 

City Park

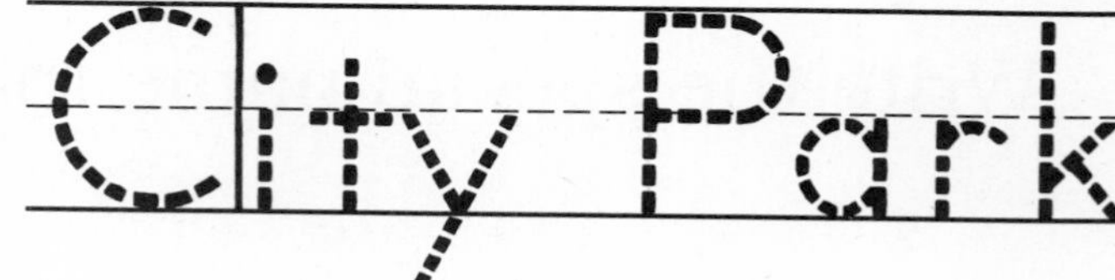

4. 

Bill

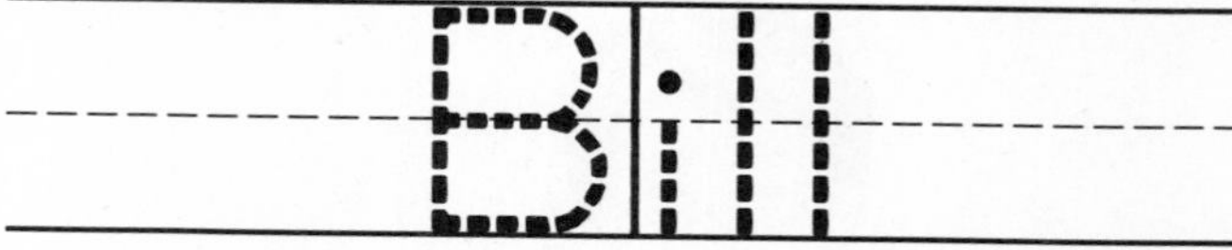

Circle the special names.

1. girl 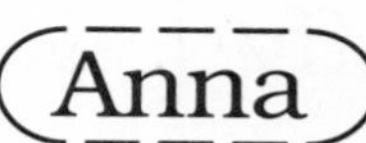

2. Pete boy

3. Kit cat

he, she, it

You know that some words are naming words.

He, **she**, and **it** can take the place of naming words.

Draw a line to **he**, **she**, or **it**.

1. Linda	she / he	Linda — she
2. grandfather	he / it	grandfather — he
3. bed	he / it	bed — it
4. kite	she / it	kite — it

Write **he**, **she**, or **it**.

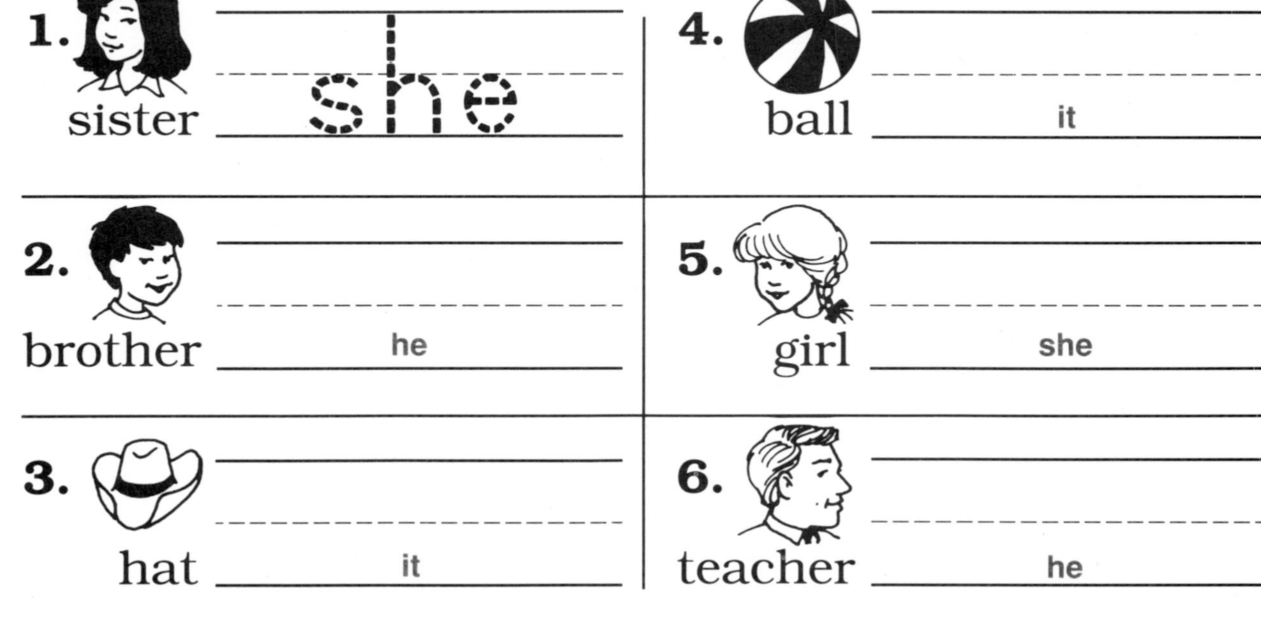

 Trace **he, she,** and **it.**

Match the words with the pictures.

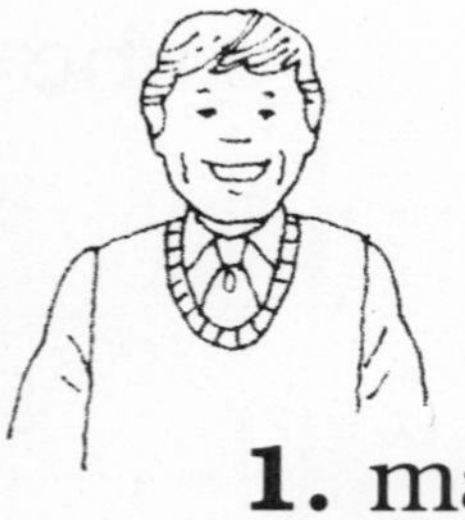

1. man — it

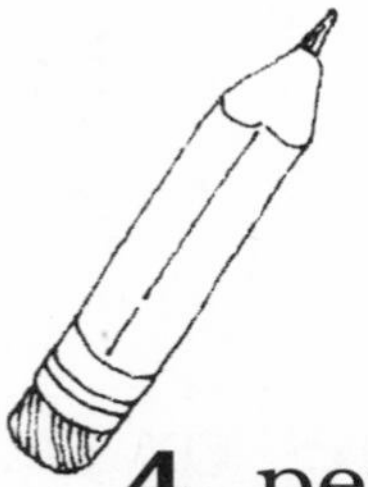

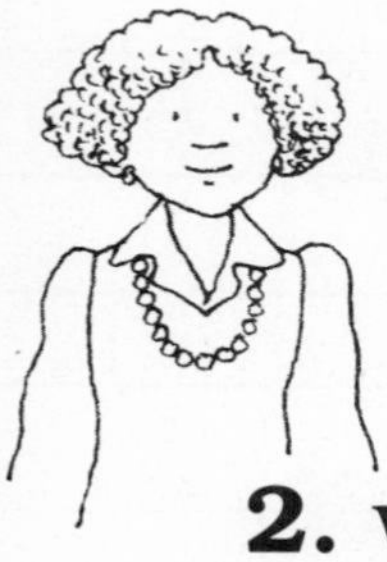

2. woman — he

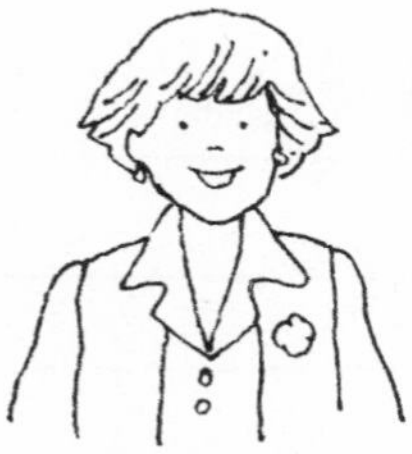

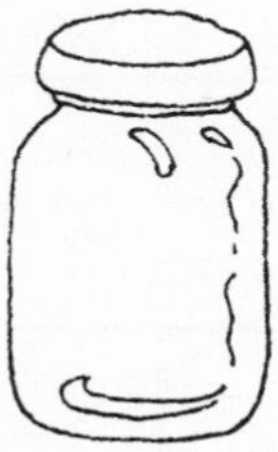

3. jar — she

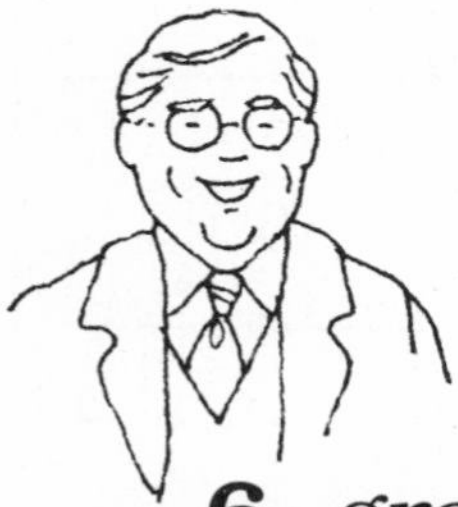

4. pencil — she

5. sister — he

6. grandfather — it

Action Words

Some words are **action words**. Some **action words** tell what people and animals do.

The boys **sing**.

Draw a line under each action word.

1. The boys run.

4. The men talk.

2. The boys hop.

5. The children laugh.

3. The girls read.

6. The girls jump.

Match the pictures with the right action words.

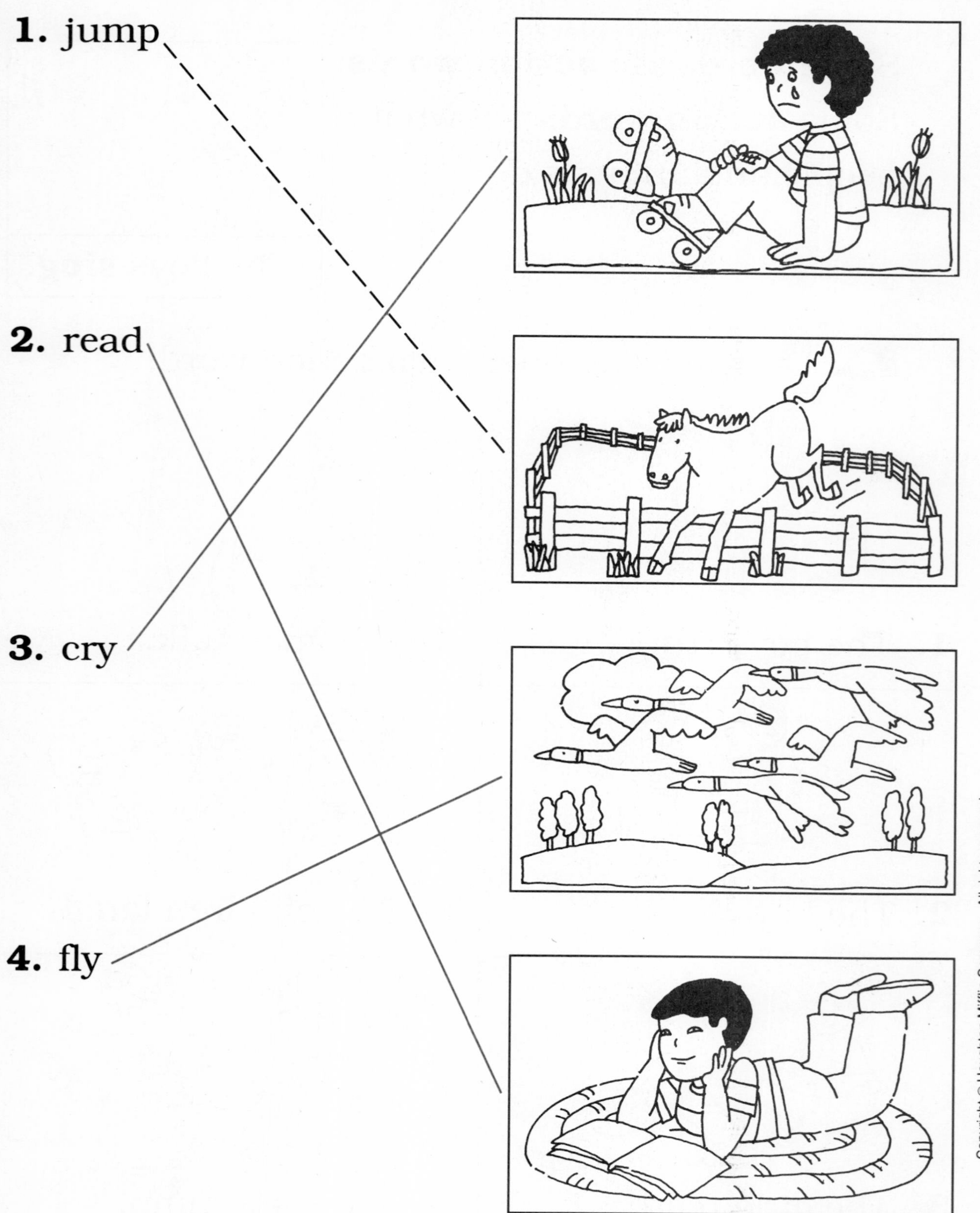

Action Words with One and More

Some action words tell about more than one.

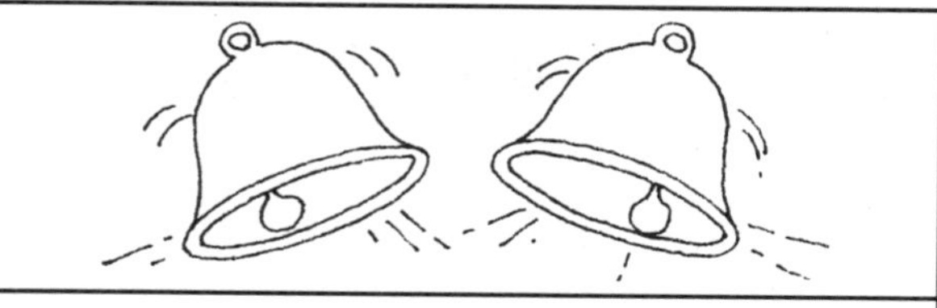

The bells ring.

Some girls jump.

Some action words tell about one.

Action words that tell about one end in **s**.

The bell ring**s**.

A girl jump**s**.

Write the action word for each picture.

1. This dog .  runs

2. The boys talk.  talk

3. My little sister sits.  sits

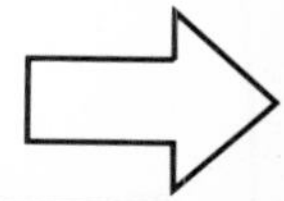

Trace the action words.

1. One frog 

.

2. Two frogs 

.

3. A fish swims.

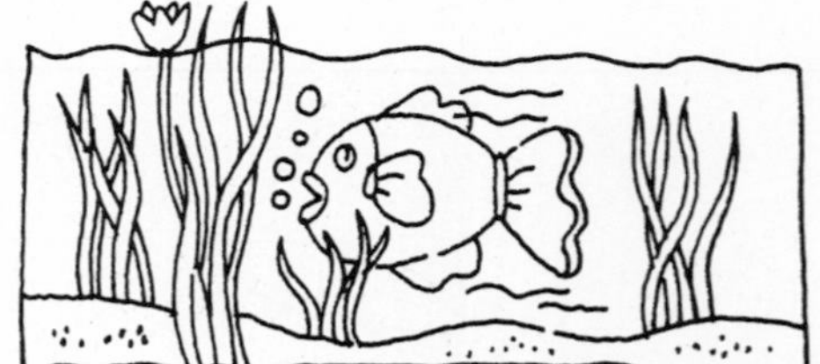

4. Two fish swim.

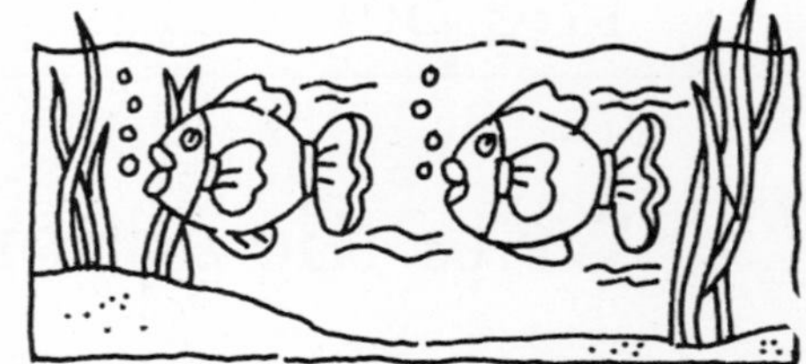

5. One girl sings.

6. Some girls 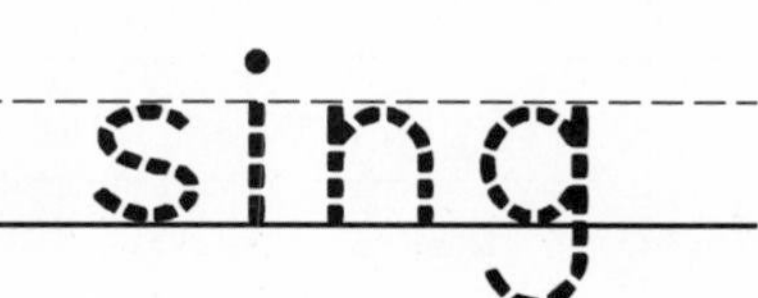

.

is and are

Use **is** in a sentence about one.

Use **are** in a sentence about more than one.

This boy **is** happy.

These boys **are** happy.

 Circle **is** or **are** to finish each sentence.

1. This girl (**is** **are**) six.

2. The bird (**is** **are**) small.

3. These girls (**is** **are**) friends.

4. Many birds (**is** **are**) here.

5. This duck (**is** **are**) big.

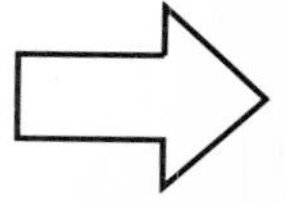

 Circle the right word in each sentence.

1. The boy (**is** **are**) tall.

2. Two boys (**is** **are**) here.

3. One duck (**is** **are**) little.

4. Two ducks (**is** **are**) big.

Adding ed

Add **ed** to some action words to tell about the past.

Now	Past
I play now. I jump today.	I play**ed** last night. I jump**ed** yesterday.

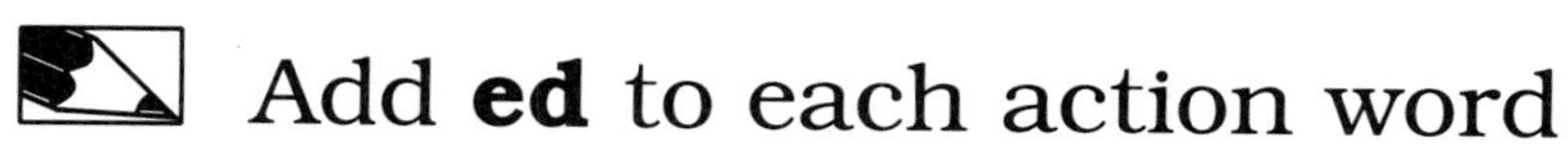

Add **ed** to each action word.

1. We painted after lunch.

2. We rest ed yesterday.

3. Last week I call ed Grandfather.

4. Yesterday Grandmother call ed.

5. Last night we walk ed home.

Write the action words that tell about the past.

called **1.** We called the cats.

jumped **2.** The cats jumped down.

walked **3.** We all walked home.

Draw a picture.

Action Words in Sentences

Some action words tell what people and animals do.

Complete each sentence with an action word from the box.

works	swims	eat	sleeps	help

1. My dog sleeps in a bed.

2. The men eat lunch.

3. I help my father.

4. A bear swims in the lake.

5. Mr. Long works at the school.

 Trace the action words to finish the sentences.

1. The girls 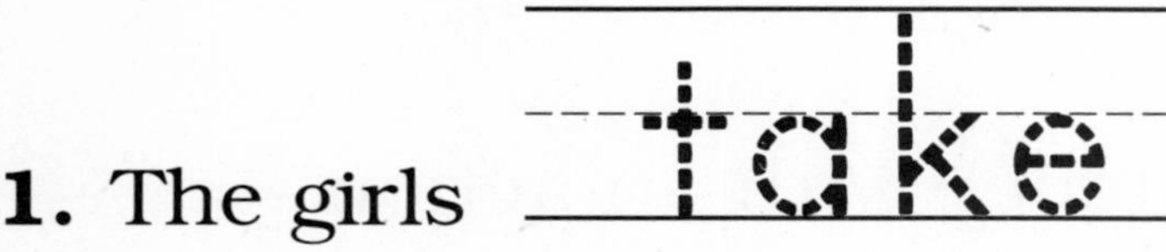 the books.

2. This fox 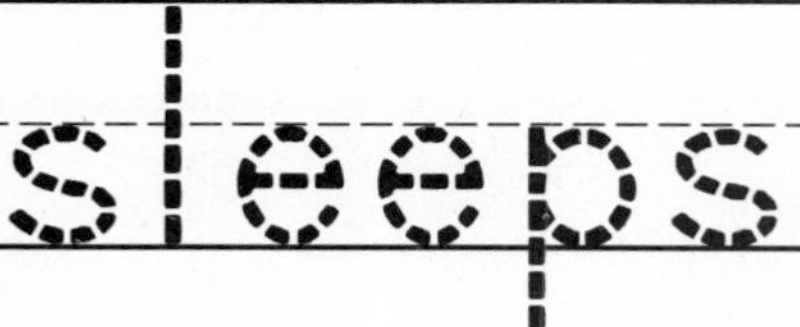 on a box.

3. My little sister .

4. We  into the room.

5. I  a pear.

<u>was</u> and <u>were</u>

Use **was** in a sentence about one.

Use **were** in a sentence about more than one.

This dog **was** in.

These dogs **were** out.

Write **was** or **were**.

1. Jan ___was___ sick.
was were

2. Ann and Rosa ___were___ asleep.
was were

3. Father ___was___ at home.
was were

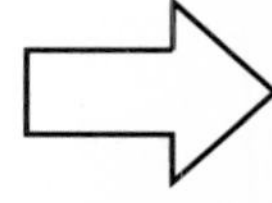

Trace **was** and **were.**

1. The rabbit 

little.

2. The bears 

big.

3. This girl was happy.

4. The boys 

sad.

5. The boat was red.

6. These trucks were green.

7. Ana was here.

8. Ted and I were there.

isn't, don't, can't

Isn't means **is not**.
Don't means **do not.**
Can't means **cannot**.

This mark ' takes the place of missing letters.

Match the words that mean the same.

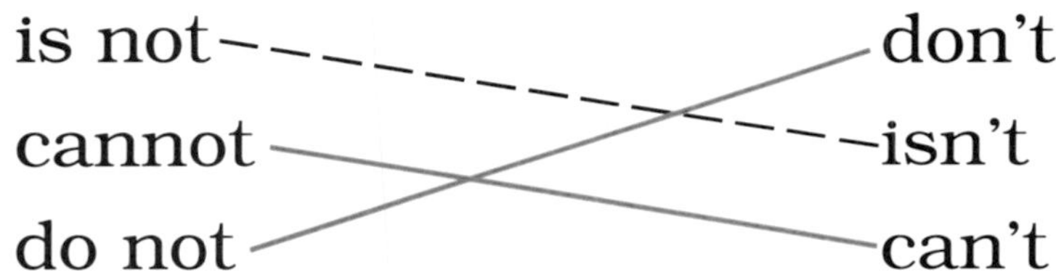

is not	don't
cannot	isn't
do not	can't

Write each word.

1. can't

2. don't

3. isn't

 Match the words.

1. is not — can't
2. cannot — don't
3. do not — isn't

 Trace the words.

1. That book isn't my book.

2. I can't find my book.

3. I don't have time to look.

Language, Mechanics, and Usage Lessons

Overview

Language, Mechanics, and Usage Lessons have been provided in the *Student Resource Book* as an optional resource for teachers who wish to integrate these skills into their reading/language arts curriculum.

The Language, Mechanics, and Usage Lessons provide opportunities for direct instruction in key language areas. Instruction, modeling, guided practice, and independent practice are provided for each skill. Children using *Houghton Mifflin Reading: The Literature Experience*, will have a rich variety of reading, writing, listening, and speaking projects and activities; this section provides a useful support for those language arts areas.

The Language, Mechanics, and Usage Lessons are organized into the following two major sections: Naming Words and Action Words.

Format of the Lessons

Each lesson is two pages in length. The first page provides instruction and guided practice. The second page provides independent practice. Instruction, written to the child, can be used as a basis for a teacher-led discussion. Suggestions for modeling each lesson can be found on pages 68–70 of the *Student Resource Book, Teacher's Annotated Edition*. Guided practice begins with an example and gives children an opportunity to practice the skill with the guidance and support of the teacher. Directions for the independent practice are clearly written and easy to follow. An example is provided to reinforce both the directions and the skill. Throughout, vocabulary has been kept at a level that allows children to focus on the skill.

How to Use the Lessons

The teacher's goals, style of teaching, and classroom organization will guide the use of this section. Because the lessons are grouped into skill categories and in many cases build sequentially, it is best to use them in the order presented. Some ideas for incorporating the lessons into your teaching plan follow.

1. You might decide to incorporate the two major sections of Language, Mechanics, and Usage Lessons into the three themes in the student anthology. For example, you could teach the lessons in the Naming Words section with the first theme; the first three lessons in the Action Words section with the second theme; and the last four lessons in the Action Words section with the third theme.
2. You might choose to use this section as a resource to supplement your own or a published instructional program in language, mechanics, and usage.
3. Annotations in the *Bookworm* Journal Teacher's Edition provide suggestions for coordinating the activities in the student Journal with lessons in this section. You might find it helpful to familiarize yourself with this section and, knowing the contents, to use those suggestions to help children who indicate in their speech or writing a need for work in a particular area.

The flexibility of this section permits it to be used in a variety of ways. You, as a teacher, will know best how to use it.

Using the Language, Mechanics, and Usage Lessons

Page 43 Naming Words

Modeling the Lesson Explain to children that they will say some naming words. Display pictures of people, animals, objects, and places, one at a time, asking volunteers to name each. Write the words on the board.

Have children make up sentences about the pictures. Write each sentence on the board. Ask volunteers to tell which words are naming words and to underline them. Help children identify the naming words.

Using the Pupil Page Help children find page 43. Read the lesson title and first line of text. Read the naming words in the word box, pointing to each word as you read it. Explain that these words name the pictures.

Direct children to the pencil and read the directions. Point out that the first naming word has been written. Ask a volunteer to tell why the naming word is correct. (*Dog* names the pictured animal.)

Point to each picture and help children identify it. Have children trace the word *dog* and then complete the exercise. Provide guidance as needed.

Page 45 Naming Words in Sentences

Modeling the Lesson Write these words as column heads on the board:

People Places Animals Things

Ask volunteers for naming words to place in each column. Then write four sentences on the board, using a naming word from each column. Read the sentences aloud. Explain to children that in this lesson they will learn to use naming words in sentences.

Using the Pupil Page Help children find page 45. Read the lesson title and definition. Direct children to the first pencil. Read the directions aloud. Then read the words in the box.

Ask children to listen carefully as you read each sentence and to decide which word is missing. The first sentence has been done. Ask a volunteer to tell why the given answer is correct. (The only naming word in the box for a pet is *cat.*) Ask children to trace this answer. Read the other sentences aloud, allowing time between sentences for children to write.

Direct children to the second pencil and read the directions. Read each sentence aloud, allowing time between sentences for children to write.

Page 47 One and More Than One

Modeling the Lesson Show a pencil and then a group of pencils. Write *pencil* and *pencils* on the board. Explain that some naming words mean one and some mean more than one. Ask children how the word that names more than one is different.

Then on the board make a list of other singular words and plural words that end with *s*. Have volunteers circle the plurals and then use these words in sentences.

Using the Pupil Page Help children find page 47. Read the lesson title and each rule. Help children notice that because there is an *s* in *boats*, there is more than one boat in the picture.

Direct children to the pencil and read the directions. Point out that there is more than one book in the picture.

Read all the words aloud. Ask children to raise their hands when they hear and see a word that means more than one. Have children complete the exercise. Provide guidance as needed.

Page 49 Special Names

Modeling the Lesson Write these naming words in a column on the board: *teacher, man, woman, doctor, city, store, dog.* Then write your name next to *teacher.* Explain that your name is a naming word, but it is a special name. It refers to you only. Circle the capital letters and explain that special names always begin with capitals.

Ask volunteers for special names to write next to *man* and *woman,* circling each capital letter. Follow the above procedure for places and animals.

Using the Pupil Page Help children find page 49. Read the lesson title and the first three statements and examples.

Have children identify the capital letters in the examples. Then read them the rule.

Direct children to the pencil. Read the directions aloud. Ask a volunteer to tell why the first answer is correct. (*Ron* is a special name; it begins with a capital letter.)

Have children trace the first answer and then complete the exercise. Provide guidance as needed.

Page 51 *he, she, it*

Modeling the Lesson Display several pictures showing boys and girls in various activities. Ask a volunteer for a sentence that describes what one child is doing in one of the pictures, such as *The boy paints.* Write the sentence on the board. Repeat it, replacing *The boy* with *He.* Do this again with a picture of a girl and the word *She.*

Using the Pupil Page Help children find page 51. Read the lesson title and the definition.

Direct children to the first pencil. Read the directions aloud. Ask a volunteer to tell why the answer to the first item is correct. (*She* takes the place of *Linda.*) Have them trace the dashed line and then complete the exercise. Provide guidance as needed.

Direct children to the second pencil and read the directions aloud. Discuss the completed item and read the other words. Have children trace the first answer and then complete the exercise. Provide guidance as needed.

Page 53 Action Words

Modeling the Lesson Explain to children that action words are special words that tell what people and animals do.

Then ask children to tell what they do at school each day. Write their responses on the board in simple sentences, such as *We read.* Emphasize the action word in each sentence by underlining it.

Using the Pupil Page Help children find page 53 and read the lesson title. Then read the definition and the example sentence in the box. Explain that *sing* is an action word that tells what the boys in the picture are doing.

Direct children to the pencil and read the directions. Ask for volunteers to tell what the children in the pictures are doing. Then read the action words that illustrate the pictures. Ask children to complete the exercise. Provide guidance as needed.

Page 55 Action Words with One and More

Modeling the Lesson Write these sentences on the board:

The girl works. The girls work.

Underline the singular naming word in the first sentence and explain that it means only one. Then draw two lines under the action word. Point out that because the naming word means only one, the action word must end with *s.*

Underline the plural naming word in the second sentence and explain that it means more than one. Then draw two lines under the action word. Point out that because the naming word means more than one, the action word does not end with *s.*

Using the Pupil Page Help children find page 55. Read the lesson title, the rules, and the example sentences. Discuss the examples with children.

Direct children to the pencil and read the directions and sentences. Have children complete the exercise. Provide guidance as needed.

Page 57 *is* and *are*

Modeling the Lesson Write these sentences on the board:

My kitten is small. My kittens are small.

Explain to children that the first sentence tells about one kitten; the second tells about more than one kitten.

Then tell children that today they will play a game using *is* and *are.* If you say *One bird is blue,* children should say *Two birds are blue.* Play this game until children understand the concept of *is* and *are.*

Write these sentences on the board:

The pencil (is, are) yellow.
The pencils (is, are) yellow.

Hold up one pencil and read the first sentence. Ask a volunteer to circle the correct word. Then repeat with more than one pencil and the second sentence.

Using the Pupil Page Help children find page 57 and read the lesson title. Read the rules and the examples. Be certain that children see the connection between the rules and the example sentences.

Direct children to the pencil and read the directions. Ask children to look at the pictures as you read the sentences. Then let children complete the exercise. Provide guidance as needed.

Page 59 Adding *-ed*

Modeling the Lesson Write these sentences on the board:

The frogs jump high.
We play ball.
I answer the phone.

Have volunteers name and underline each action word. (jump, play, ball)

Point out that these sentences tell about now. Explain that when we talk about the past, action words sound and look different. Then repeat the sentences in the past tense. Ask volunteers to tell the difference. (The sound for *d* was added at the end.)

Then add *-ed* to each of the verbs on the board. Read the sentences aloud. Point out and explain that most action words that tell what happened in the past have *-ed* at the end.

Using the Pupil Page Help children find page 59. Read the lesson title, the rule, and the examples. Then direct children to the pencil and read the directions.

Ask children whether the action word in each numbered sentence tells about now or about the past. Then let them complete the exercise. Provide guidance as needed.

Page 61 Action Words in Sentences

Modeling the Lesson Ask a volunteer to tell what an action word does in a sentence. (It tells what the naming word does.) Explain to children that you will say a naming part and they will turn it into a sentence by adding an action word. If you say *The tiger,* they should say an action word such as *eats* or *walks.*

When children understand the procedure, have them make sentences with these naming parts: *A kitten, The dog, Some frogs, Our pet.*

Using the Pupil Page Help children find page 61. Read the lesson title and rule. Direct children to the pencil and read the directions. Then read the action words in the box. Ask for a volunteer to tell what the *s* at the end of some action words means. (The action word tells about one.)

Read the first sentence and discuss why *sleeps* is the correct answer. (It makes sense added to the rest of the words; it ends with an *s*.) Then have children complete the exercise. Provide guidance as needed.

Page 63 *was* and *were*

Modeling the Lesson Review with children that *is* and *are* tell about things that are happening now. Then write the following sentences on the board:

One bird was in the nest.
Four birds were in the nest.

Explain to children that *was* and *were* tell about what happened in the past. Lead children to realize that *was* tells about one and *were* tells about more than one.

Using the Pupil Page Help children find page 63. Read the lesson title and the rules. Then ask volunteers to read the example sentences. Discuss the pictures and the use of *was* and *were.*

Direct children to the pencil and read the directions. Then read the numbered sentences. Have children complete the exercise. Provide guidance as needed.

Page 65 *isn't, don't, can't*

Modeling the Lesson Write *isn't, don't,* and *can't* on the board. Beneath each contraction write the words from which it was made: *is not, do not,* and *cannot.*

Read these words and explain that they have the same meanings as the contractions. Ask volunteers to tell which letters are missing in the contractions. Circle those letters. Point to the apostrophes. Explain that the apostrophe takes the place of missing letters.

Using the Pupil Page Help children find page 65. Read the lesson title and the definitions of *isn't, don't, can't,* and the apostrophe.

Direct children to the first pencil. Read the directions and the exercise words. Ask a volunteer to tell why the first match is correct. (*Isn't* means *is not.*) Have children trace the line. Then let them complete the exercise. Provide guidance as needed.

Direct children to the second pencil. Read the directions and the exercise words. Discuss the pictures. Then have children complete the exercise. Provide guidance as needed.